A Practical Manual for Party Wall Surveyors

A Practical Manual for Party Wall Surveyors

John Anstey BA, FRICS, FCIArb

Edited by

Graham North ARICS, ACIArb

RICS BOOKS

Figures 2, 3, 9, 10, 11 and 12 have been reproduced by kind permission of Victor H. Vegoda (Vegoda and Company Limited)

Please note: References to the masculine include, where appropriate, the feminine.

Published by RICS Business Services Limited, a wholly owned subsidiary of
The Royal Institution of Chartered Surveyors,
under the RICS Books imprint
Surveyor Court
Westwood Business Park
Coventry CV4 8JE
UK

ISBN 1 84219 007 5

Cover design by Nooode
Typeset in Great Britain by Wyvern 21 Ltd., Bristol
Printed in Great Britain by J. W. Arrowsmith Ltd., Bristol

Contents

	Author details	6
	Foreword	7
	Introduction	8
Chapter 1:	Taking instructions	9
Chapter 2:	Tracing ownerships	13
Chapter 3:	Establishing what works are included	15
Chapter 4:	Serving notice	17
Chapter 5:	Checking a notice received (and sending any counter-notices)	25
Chapter 6:	Obtaining/giving consent	30
Chapter 7:	Appointing surveyors	32
Chapter 8:	Selecting the third surveyor	36
Chapter 9:	The schedule of condition	38
Chapter 10:	Communications	43
Chapter 11:	Change of ownership	46
Chapter 12:	The extent of a surveyor's authority	49
Chapter 13:	The award	51
Chapter 14:	Third surveyors and appeals	56
Chapter 15:	Fees and expenses	59
Chapter 16:	The progress of the works	63
Appendix 1:	Definitions	66
Appendix 2:	Further reading and information	72
	Index	74

Author details

John Anstey BA, FRICS, FCIArb, had 35 years' experience as a party wall surveyor, and was deeply involved in drafting and seeing through Parliament the Party Wall etc. Act 1996. He had already written, edited and contributed to numerous books about party walls but felt that there was still a gap to be filled: this manual is written to fill this gap. The manual provides a blow-by-blow practical guide through all the stages of party wall work, from the first approach of a building owner to final making good and payment of fees.

John Anstey sadly died before this book could be published and it has therefore been edited by Graham North, one of John's Partners in the firm of Anstey, Horne & Company.

Foreword

I feel privileged to be invited to write a short introduction to this book, but the sense of loss at the death of a friend and colleague remains. I am also delighted that it has been decided to publish this manual. It was John's latest, and last, contribution to the fund of knowledge and learning he had made available to practising party wall surveyors. He revised the manual whilst he was 'convalescing' after a heart attack, and it was fitting testament to his willpower and enthusiasm.

This is a practical manual, written as a complement to John's previous books on the subject (see p. 72). It is a working guide, designed to assist surveyors, architects and engineers to adopt a proper logical and systematic approach to dealing with party wall procedures.

In addition to his writings, with the help of a handful of surveyors from the Pyramus and Thisbe Club (see p. 72) and with the support of the Earl of Lytton in ensuring the Party Wall Bill came through the House of Lords, John was the prime motivator behind the passing of the Party Wall etc. Act 1996. Whilst many people had a hand in drafting and ensuring that the Bill was passed, few spent the time and emotional effort necessary to achieve the aim of ensuring that owners throughout England and Wales were protected in relation to works adjoining the boundary.

In common with all John's writing, this manual is eminently readable, and bears testimony to his dedication to raising standards and education in its widest sense. He had a brilliant mind, coupled with an ability to translate complicated problems into everyday language.

I first met him in the early 1970s, and we quickly became constant professional opponents, firm friends and professional colleagues. I said at his memorial service that his whole approach to professional practice was that of problem solving. Whether the problem was on his side or yours made no difference, and I can recall no case where a solution was not eventually found.

Adoption of this manual should enable all practitioners to follow that example. It is of equal value to the relatively inexperienced, the experienced, and indeed to the over experienced. Above all it adopts a practical approach, and the text is relevant and accurate.

Eric Roe FRICS

Introduction

Party wall legislation has existed in London for over 300 years (and was also known in ancient civilization). It culminated in the London Building Acts (Amendment) Act 1939 and was very popular with surveyors and property owners in the old County of London. Many people outside London expressed a wish to share the benefits of this legislation, and so a working party drafted, and eventually saw through Parliament, a Bill to extend party wall law to the whole of England and Wales.

Following the coming into force of the Party Wall etc. Act 1996, several books dealing with the law on the subject have been published: some good, some bad and some wicked. My own book, *Party Walls and What to do with Them* (published by RICS Books) was completely rewritten as a fourth edition (and is now in a further revised fifth edition) and is a more general guide to what happens when party walls have to be dealt with. However, even that book is not perhaps a manual with which the novice surveyor can hope to navigate his way through any difficulties which actually arise in practice. Therefore it is hoped that this slender volume will fill that gap in an expanding library for an expanding field of work.

Let me stress right at the outset, however, that the Act was designed not to make work (and money) for surveyors, but to ease the resolution of disputes between neighbours. Indeed, the very existence of the Act may prevent disputes altogether, just as the ultimate sanction of a court order under the Access to Neighbouring Land Act 1992 has persuaded people to allow their next door neighbours to come on to their land to carry out maintenance or repair, without making undue difficulty or objection – at least, I hope it has. Certainly, this Act does not get much use, which is not true of the Party Wall Act.

You may be wondering about the 'etc.' part of the Act. Well, during the drafting process Parliamentary Counsel complained that the Bill dealt with matters beyond party walls and even suggested calling it the Neighbouring Land Act. I jokingly suggested calling it the Party Wall etc. Bill and to my astonishment the title was adopted. It duly received the Royal Assent in July 1996 and came fully into force in September 1997.

CHAPTER 1

Taking instructions

The building owner

The building owner, under the Party Wall etc. Act 1996, is very precisely defined. When someone approaches you to act for them as their surveyor, it is essential that you should find out whether they qualify. At one time this was important at even the domestic level, when Mr Herman lost an expensive legal action because he and Mrs Herman were joint owners of their house, but only he had signed the party structure notice. This occurred under the London Building Acts, however, and the authors of the new Act changed the wording to avoid that particular difficulty. In the case of residential properties, there is rarely any doubt as to the status of the owner, but in commercial cases, the situation is not so simple.

The definition of 'owner' is stated to include various categories, so it is not exclusive, but clearly all those mentioned are covered. The most important things to note are that yearly tenancies or less do not count, and that an agreement for a lease or a contract to purchase both qualify as ownership. The building owner is the person doing the work, and the adjoining owner is the person next door. The common mistake is for a group ('So-And-So Properties') to 'instruct' a surveyor to serve notice and then, much later, to mention that the property is legally owned by 'So-And-So Properties Thingy Street Ltd'. It is essential, therefore, that in response to the very first approach from the owner of a building you should ascertain the correct legal ownership of the building in question, and the status of the owner.

Some owners are rather apt to jump the gun, but until they are at least under contract they are not entitled to serve notice. That does not prevent a surveyor from advising them about the Act, notices, etc., so that they will be ready to serve notice just as soon as they have signed their contract.

At this stage, whether there is an owner under the Act or not, the surveyor is not a 'party wall surveyor'. As you will see in later chapters, that appointment cannot occur until a dispute has arisen, deemed or actual, between owners, but for now the parties are in the normal client/agent relationship. The surveyor is free to give partial advice to his client, and can try to avoid unnecessary expenditure on party wall matters by recommending changes in the design or procedures. Remembering Construction (Design and Management) (CDM) regulations, the party wall surveyor should avoid actually designing anything himself. If the matter proceeds this will all change, although the building owner's surveyor may still be called upon to act as adviser to the owner, as well as fulfilling his impartial role as surveyor under the Act.

The surveyor must find out exactly what is proposed by the building owner (see chapter three for more details). It is also recommended that he is armed with a letter of authority, empowering him to carry out many of the functions that you might expect to be exercised by the actual building owner, especially the signing and service of notice and the appointment of other surveyors (see *Figure 1*). Experience has shown that it is much more efficient for the surveyor to carry out these tasks (more detail will be given on this subject in the appropriate place).

The appointment of a surveyor must be in writing, as laid down in section 10 (2) of the Act, and before taking any action under the Act, a surveyor must have received the appropriate letter from the owner. This is particularly true if he intends to serve notice on the owner's behalf.

Let me conclude this section by saying again that the essentials at this stage are to ensure that:

1. instructions come from the correct source;
2. they are in writing;
3. the surveyor knows more or less what the building owner has in mind; and
4. the surveyor is properly authorized to deal with ensuing matters.

The adjoining owner

Ascertaining the status of an adjoining owner should not be as difficult as determining the building owner. It is, in any case, the responsibility

7 Church Street
Wimbledon
London
SW19 7AA

31 July 1997

Dear Mr Anstey

Re: Party Wall etc. Act 1996

You are hereby authorized to sign, serve and receive any notices in connection with the works proposed at the above address. In the event of a dispute arising and there being no agreed surveyor appointment, I appoint you, Mr Anstey, in accordance with section 10 of the Act as my surveyor. I also authorize you to make any necessary appointment under that Section on my behalf.

Yours sincerely

Mrs Jane Smith

Figure 1: Draft letter of authority

of the building owner to find and identify the adjoining owner on whom he serves notice (a duty probably devolved on his surveyor). However, if you accept instructions and carry out works on behalf of someone who turns out to be a monthly tenant, you may have a little difficulty recovering your fees. After all, if your owner is not an 'owner', you are not a 'surveyor' under the Act and therefore cannot use its procedures to recover those fees. Just to remind you, an owner must have more than a yearly tenancy, and must either adjoin the other property or be within three or six metres of it if the works proposed go below his building. This will be explained in more detail later (see chapter three).

However, get it in writing. The old adage, 'do right, and fear no man; don't write, and fear no woman' can be adapted for party wall purposes: 'do right and fear no client, don't write, and you're not a party wall surveyor'. (I know that is not quite right, but you get my drift.)

What you have to do when you have accepted the appointment is dealt with later, along with advice on when to refuse the appointment.

CHAPTER 2

Tracing ownerships

I have already dealt with the difficulty of ensuring that you know who your instructing owner is. Now we have got to find out, for the owner, who all the adjoining owners are. You can, of course, satisfy the Act simply by addressing notices to 'the owner', but this can lead to difficulties (as we shall see in chapter four). Also, it makes for much better personal relationships if you address the neighbour by name.

At the domestic level, you probably know who your neighbour is – though I always struggle for surnames, or ask my wife – or your client will tell you. If you really do not know, the electoral register may help. At the commercial level, you are much more likely to be dealing with multiple occupation and proliferating ownership. As already pointed out, the definition of 'owner' is quite wide, and there may be more than one owner of an adjoining building – freeholder, long leaseholder and occupying tenant. In city centre properties three owners is quite common, and there can occasionally be more. If you can find out who the managing agents are they will generally be able – and sometimes willing – to give you the necessary information.

When the adjacent property is an office block or block of flats (and sometimes just a pair of maisonettes) there is the additional problem of finding out how many of the occupiers are 'adjoining'. Some occupiers may be intimately involved with the proposed works, and some may be on the far side of the building, with no reason to be notified. Who needs to be served with a notice will be dealt with shortly (see chapter three).

There can be no harm in going round personally – or by assistant – to find out who lives or works next door. Sometimes a list on the doorway will tell you – although do not make the mistake of thinking that firms whose registered offices are listed are all occupiers. Very often there will be a small plaque giving the name of the freeholder, but sometimes even the people you can find to talk to will not know who it is, or even if there is more than one interest above them. In this situation only formal communication will produce the answers, possibly via an agent.

When dealing with big blocks, there is the additional problem of deciding which parts of a building are affected, and which occupiers inhabit those parts. Even when you have found out which flats, or which sets of offices, are on the side of the building which your client's works will abut, you have to decide how many of those premises will actually be affected by the works or need notice (as to which type of notice, see chapter four).

You must be diligent in seeking out all the owners who are entitled to notice. Failure to serve notice on one of them at the outset could result in a two-month delay in the middle of the works. While a mistake is not necessarily negligence, it is very hard to convince the courts that you have made a non-negligent mistake. Therefore, you may be liable for damages to your client if you have carelessly failed to identify an adjoining owner who should have received notice.

When I write to an adjoining owner, by name or description, I always ask whether there is anyone from whom they hold or holding under them. That way I can certainly claim to have tried to find other interests.

CHAPTER 3
Establishing what works are included

The greatest difficulty is usually encountered when trying to find out whether three or six metre notices are going to be needed. (As to when they are, see chapter four.) For those purposes, however, you need to know how deep next door's foundations are. To do this you can ask the occupier; you can check records at the local authority (quite often someone on the professional team will actually know the building); you can guess or you can dig. What is certain is that you must have some sort of idea of the depth.

If you have to dig, beware of doing so in such a way that even your exploration needs notice. Opinion is divided on this subject, but I think that a man, a spade, and a barrow are not 'excavating' within the meaning of the Act. A planked and strutted excavation, however, is self-evidently within the Act. Do not be afraid of guessing. A good building surveyor will probably know approximately how deep the foundations are to most standard types of house. Commercial buildings are much more variable.

Next you must find out how deep your foundations are going. The architect will not know, and will refer you to the engineer. The engineer will not have decided yet. You must persuade him to give you his best estimate, because your notice depends on it. You need to know how far from the next door building your nearest foundation will be, and approximately how deep it will be. If the engineer changes his mind later, no one will mind, as long as valid notice has been served. If he causes a notice to be served late in the programme by moving the foundations nearer or deeper he will not be popular – but the party wall surveyor will probably be blamed. The latter must therefore be aware of this when trying to get information from the engineer in the first place.

Now, as forewarned, you must decide who is affected by the works – what we call 'the bicycle shed against Dolphin Square' syndrome. If you are doing works at ground floor level, is any effect going to be felt on the first floor? If you are raising a new fourth floor on an existing third, will the adjoining second (and any lower) floor need notice? There is no definitive answer to these questions, but you must ask yourself not just whether notice is needed – it probably will not be, in law – but whether it is actually likely (or possible) that there will be some physical effect, in which case unofficial notice may well be desirable. By 'unofficial notice' I mean a letter telling the other owners about the proposed works, offering to take a schedule of condition if there is a real possibility of damage – or allegations of damage. You should have your client's (note the word) approval for such activities. When deciding whether separately occupied areas need even unofficial notice it may be helpful – though difficult – if you can find out the repairing responsibilities for the fabric.

In order for you to perform the next task (serving notices) properly, you must fully understand the works proposed and their relation to the adjoining building. Unless your notice gives a reasonably clear description of the works proposed, the notice will not be valid. In order to know what kind of works need a notice, read the Act carefully; then read it again. I do not intend to reproduce chunks of the Act in this manual, so you will need to refer to the Act itself or one of the other publications that do include the Act, such as *The Green Book* (published by The Pyramus and Thisbe Club).

CHAPTER 4
Serving notice

Different actions need different forms of notice, but no notices need printed forms. You will find examples of these forms later in this chapter and you may well find it convenient to use these or the ones recommended by the RICS or The Pyramus and Thisbe Club, especially for commercial jobs, but do not let anyone tell you that they are essential. As I shall demonstrate shortly, they are not. There are three different types of notice, depending on the state of the boundary or the works proposed. Section 1 of the Act deals with line of junction notices, with very little built there at present; section 2 is the most important section, since it deals with attacks on an existing party wall (notice is actually given under section 3); and section 6 deals with foundation notices.

I have assumed that you have a copy of the Act (or *The Green Book*), so I will not spell out all the works in respect of which you might want to serve notice. This chapter is about the actual service.

Section 1 of the Act deals with the situation where there is no wall astride the boundary, or only a garden wall on one side of the boundary. If the building owner (the one who intends to do some work) wants to build a wall astride the boundary, either a party wall (forming part of a building) or a party fence wall (a garden wall), he has to give the adjoining owner one month's notice and describe the proposed wall.

If the adjoining owner does not agree with the proposal, or if the building owner intends to build only on his own land, abutting the boundary, the latter must again give the same period of notice. The difference is that the adjoining owner cannot really object, not even to footings projecting across the boundary on to his land (as long as they are not reinforced). Since refusal to assent to the first type of notice necessitates the service of the second type of notice, if time is of the essence it would seem desirable to serve both notices at the outset, one without prejudice to the other.

Although the building owner can do – more or less – what he likes on his own land, it is possible – but unlikely – that disputes will arise under this section. If they do, however, they are subject to section 10 of the Act just like any other dispute.

As I have already said, section 2 of the Act is the most important section, and you should carefully check which sub-sections and paragraphs apply to the works intended.

Section 3 is much more specific in what it requires to be given by way of information if work is intended under section 2. The building owner must give his name and address, describe the works, and say when he intends to start the works. Without this information there can be no doubt that any purported notice is invalid. There are leading cases to say that insufficient description of the works, or inaccurate information as to the building owner, will disqualify the notice.

Section 6 also requires the service of notice, either because the building owner's foundations are going to be lower than next door's and within three metres of them (see *Figure 2*), or because they are within six metres and they are going to intersect a 45° angle from the bottom of next door's foundations (see *Figure 3*) (for the precise detail see the Act). Although not so precise in its requirements with regard to the name and address of the building owner, additional information is needed under this section. You must supply plans and sections showing the depth of any proposed excavation and say what you intend to do to ensure that no harm comes to the foundations of the property next door. Failure to supply any of the required information again invalidates the notice.

I will repeat here what I have already said when dealing with identifying the proposed works: if the engineer (usually) cannot say exactly how deep the foundations will be, you must nevertheless give your best estimate.

Do not forget that there may be more than one adjoining owner to be served, and be aware that the word 'adjoin' has a special meaning under section 6. Any owner within the specified distances 'adjoins', whether the premises physically abut or are separated by a strip of land belonging to someone else.

We now turn to how service is carried out. Section 15 tells you that you can send a notice by post, deliver it in person, send it to the registered or head office of a company, give it to someone on the adjoining property, or affix it prominently on the premises – for example by a drawing pin to the front door. In some of the seedier parts of big cities

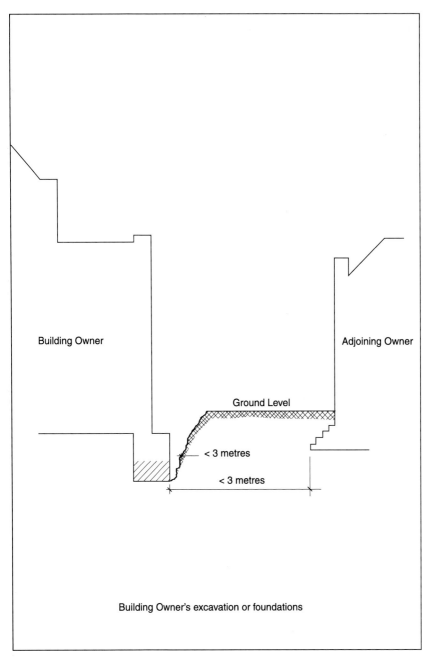

Figure 2: Three metre notice diagram

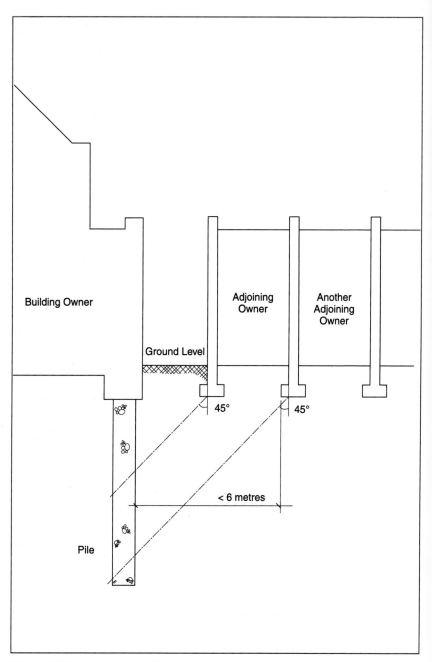

Figure 3: Six metre notice diagram

it can be very difficult to find owners, and the drawing pin comes in very handy to prove service, especially if you have the action photographed and the photograph dated.

As you know, you can simply address your notice to 'the owner', if you have been unable to identify anyone specific (see chapter two). However, if you do this in writing to a house which appears to be in single ownership, and it turns out to be two leasehold flats with an absentee freeholder, two out of the three owners are likely to be left without notice. Even if you include – as I do – a request to be informed of any other interests it may well go unanswered. Make every effort to find out how many owners make five.

I said at the beginning of this chapter that you do not need to use anyone's printed forms to serve notice, and I will now explain why and when you may well use no form at all, although for the ordinary run of commercial jobs I do in fact strongly advise you to copy an established precedent. For domestic jobs, on the other hand, I recommend that you (if you are the owner) or your client (if you are the surveyor) should write an ordinary letter to the neighbour, making sure that you give all the required details (see *Figures 4, 5* and *6*).

The purpose of the Act is not to provide work for surveyors, but to regulate works on walls between neighbours, and if disputes do arise, to provide a cheap and simple method of resolution. Consent, however, is the first aim, and it is my view that a neighbour is far more likely to consent to an informal, friendly letter from next door than to an official – if not officious – looking form.

Whichever type of notice you decide upon, be very careful about dates. Because you must give the requisite period of notice, if you pick a firm date which is one month or two months ahead when you choose it, and then time slips for any reason in the actual service so that the recipient does not have the notice the necessary time before the stated date, your notice will be invalid. It is far safer to say 'I give you one/two months' notice', or words to that effect.

You may think that I am spending a lot of time on a comparatively unimportant part of the Act. I would point out, however, that if your notice is invalid for any reason, everything that follows is void. The surveyors cannot be properly appointed, their award will be of no effect, and your works may well be illegal. Before you serve, check your notice again.

THE PARTY WALL ETC. ACT 1996
LINE OF JUNCTION NOTICE

To:

of:

as adjoining owner/s under the Act of the premises known as:

I/We:

of:

as building owner/s under the Act of:

which adjoins your premises known as

HEREBY SERVE YOU WITH NOTICE

Under section 1 (2)

that if you consent in writing it is intended to build on the line of junction of the said properties a party wall/party fence wall/or, if you are not prepared to agree to this, then/

Under section 1 (5)

that it is intended to build on the line of junction of the said properties a wall wholly on my/our land.

Under section 1 (6)

that it is intended to place projecting footings and foundations on your land at my/our expense.

Under section 7 (4)

that with your written consent, it is proposed to use special foundations.

The proposed works as shown on the accompanying drawings/are:

It is intended to commence works after one month or earlier by agreement. In the event of matters arising for settlement, section 10 of the Act requires that both parties should concur in the appointment of a surveyor, or should each appoint one surveyor, and in those circumstances I/we would appoint   of   as my/our surveyor.

Signed

authorized to sign on behalf of   building owner/s

Date:

Figure 4: Line of junction notice

THE PARTY WALL ETC. ACT 1996
PARTY STRUCTURE NOTICE

To:
of:
as adjoining owner/s under the Act of the premises known as:

I/We:
of:
as building owner/s under the Act of:
which adjoins your premises

HEREBY SERVE YOU WITH NOTICE
THAT, IN ACCORDANCE WITH MY/OUR RIGHTS:

Under section 2 sub-section (2) (a) (b) (c) (d) (e) (f) (g) (h) (i) (j) (k) (l) (m) (n) and with reference to the PARTY STRUCTURE / PARTY WALL / PARTY FENCE WALL separating the above premises, it is intended to carry out the works detailed below, after the expiration of two months from service of this notice.

The proposed works are:

It is intended to commence works when notice has run or earlier by agreement.

Under section 5, if you do not consent to the works within 14 days you are deemed to have dissented and a dispute is deemed to have arisen. In that case section 10 of the Act requires that both parties should concur in the appointment of a surveyor, or should each appoint one surveyor, and in those circumstances I/we would appoint   of
as my/our surveyor.

Signed
authorized to sign on behalf of   building owner/s

Date:

Figure 5: Party structure notice

THE PARTY WALL ETC. ACT 1996
THREE METRE/SIX METRE NOTICE

To:

of:

as adjoining owner/s under the Act of the premises known as:

I/We:

of:

as building owner/s under the Act of:

which adjoins your premises

HEREBY SERVE YOU WITH NOTICE
THAT, IN ACCORDANCE WITH MY/OUR RIGHTS:

Under section 6 (1) it is intended to build within 3 metres of your building and to a lower level than the bottom of your foundations, by carrying out the works detailed below, after the expiration of one month from service of this notice.

or

Under section 6 (2) it is intended to build within 6 metres of your building and to a depth as defined in the Act, by carrying out the works detailed below, after the expiration of one month from service of this notice.

IT IS/IS NOT PROPOSED TO UNDERPIN OR OTHERWISE STRENGHTEN IN ORDER TO SAFEGUARD THE FOUNDATIONS OF YOUR BUILDING.

The accompanying plans and sections numbered .... show the site and the excavation depth proposed.

The proposed works are:

It is intended to commence works when notice has run or earlier by agreement.

Under section 6 (7), if you do not consent to the works within 14 days you are deemed to have dissented and a dispute is deemed to have arisen. In that case section 10 of the Act requires that both parties should concur in the appointment of a surveyor, or should each appoint one surveyor, and in those circumstances I/we would appoint   of
                                    as my/our surveyor.

Signed

authorized to sign on behalf of   building owner/s

Date:

Figure 6: Three metre/six metre notice

CHAPTER 5

Checking a notice received (and sending any counter-notices)

When an adjoining owner receives a notice that seems at all complicated he will, if he is wise, discuss it forthwith with a surveyor: an unwise owner will discuss it with a solicitor. I say he is unwise to do this because it is extremely unlikely that the surveyor will eventually award him any fees for such legal discussions, and even less likely that the solicitor will not charge him fees, so he will be out of pocket. I also say 'discuss' because he should not immediately 'appoint' a surveyor. He may be advised that it is perfectly safe to consent to the works or to agree to a single surveyor, especially if a respectable one has been named in the building owner's notice, all of which is explained in more detail shortly (see chapter six).

If, after a preliminary discussion, the surveyor considers that the adjoining owner should be thinking about dissenting from the works, the surveyor should ask his prospective appointing owner to send him the notice and any accompanying papers – or at least copies thereof. When he receives the notice he should examine it meticulously. When an adjoining owner's surveyor picks holes in a notice he is not being obstructive to the building owner or his surveyor – at least, not necessarily. If the notice is defective, then everything that flows from it is equally defective: the appointment of surveyors, the award, the works – in more senses than one. It is actually helpful for the adjoining owner's surveyor to detect any error at this stage. To ignore the defect, and when the works are about to start, then to dispute the validity of the notice: that is being obstructive.

The surveyor should therefore ensure that the information required by the Act to be given is all there; and specifically that any plans which need to accompany a section 6 notice have been provided. If the notice is signed by the building owner's surveyor, the adjoining owner's surveyor should ask to see that surveyor's letter of authority to do so. He should ensure that any description of the works is adequate to understand exactly what is proposed – it has been held that a vague statement such as 'works under section 2' is not sufficient. The section 6 plans must show the site of the works and the depth of the proposed excavation. If they do not, the notice should be politely but firmly rejected. (see *Figures 7 and 8*)

Having ensured that the notice is correct, the actual or potential adjoining owner's surveyor must consider his advice to the owner. Should he consent? This will be covered in a little more detail shortly (see chapter six). What counter measures may be needed? The Act has a whole section (section 4) on 'counter-notices', and they crop up again in section 11 (although they are very rarely formally served).

Section 11 (7) is a new enactment, and has not yet been tested very much. However, section 4 re-enacts the 1939 provisions, and was not used a great deal under that legislation. It provides that the adjoining owner may require the building owner to carry out certain other works, for the adjoining owner's benefit, while the building owner is doing his own, but in fact these things are more often arranged between the surveyors and incorporated in the award. If it is obvious at the outset that they would be beneficial, it cannot be wrong for the adjoining owner to serve formally.

Security for expenses is a matter much more likely to arise, which must be dealt with at this stage. Section 12 requires the adjoining owner to give notice requiring security before the building owner 'begins any work'. Prompt action is therefore necessary if the financial arrangements are to be made in time. Security is not in case a window gets broken: it is in case the adjoining owner gets exposed – sometimes literally – to any unreasonable financial risk in restoring the status quo, should the building owner default during the works. Two questions therefore have to be asked. First, is there any risk in the works, such as demolishing a party wall which will have to be rebuilt? Second, is there anything risky about the building owner, such as his being an offshore company?

The adjoining owner himself has to request security, unless he has specifically authorized his surveyor or other agent to do so. It is not usual for this authority to be delegated, because if the owner has to write a letter dealing with the matter at all, he might as well write to his opposite number, requesting the security. However, agreement on the amount of security is a matter for the surveyors if the owners cannot agree the amount. The easiest way of dealing with it is to require the building owner to place a sum of money in a special account, in his own name, which can only be dealt with on the signatures of two of the three

---

THE PARTY WALL ETC. ACT 1996
ACKNOWLEDGEMENT OF PARTY STRUCTURE NOTICE

I/We:

of:

having received the notice served by:

of:

in respect of:

which adjoins my/our premises known as:

and in relation to the works proposed under section 2 (2), paragraphs ...

hereby CONSENT to the above works

or

hereby DISSENT from the above works and concur in the appointment of/appoint as a surveyor:

of:

Signed
authorized to sign on behalf of   adjoining owner/s

Date:

Figure 7: Acknowledgement of party structure notice

THE PARTY WALL ETC. ACT 1996
ACKNOWLEDGEMENT OF THREE/SIX METRE NOTICE

I/We:

of:

as adjoining owner/s under the Act of the premises known as:

having received the notice served by:

of:

in respect of:

which adjoins my/our premises

hereby CONSENT to the proposed works

or

require you to safeguard or underpin the foundations of my/our building

or

dispute the necessity for underpinning or strengthening the foundations of my/our building

and a dispute having arisen concur in the appointment of/appoint as a surveyor:

of:

Signed
authorized to sign on behalf of   adjoining owner/s

Date:

Figure 8: Acknowledgement of three/six metre notice

surveyors. The third surveyor is an umpire selected by the first two (see chapter eight for more details about the third surveyor). Any interest belongs to the building owner.

Be careful about the wording of the bank's form of mandate. The surveyors are only responsible for disbursing these specific funds, and should be aware of the banks' favourite forms, which make them liable for overdrafts on other accounts in the same name, and similarly ridiculous undertakings.

CHAPTER 6

Obtaining/giving consent

Consent should be given to minor works which do not expose an adjoining owner to any noticeable risk. The full panoply of the Act should not be invoked for the insertion of a flashing, or similarly small and inoffensive actions. You cannot, of course, take advantage of your rights under the Act without serving notice, but that notice should not necessarily provoke a 'dispute'.

How then should a building owner set about fulfilling the formalities in such a way as to encourage a neighbour to consent, which is highly desirable on the domestic sort of job? In my opinion, it is essential to make a personal approach. You must have with you the written notice, but if at all possible you should deliver it in person. You can then explain how insignificant the works proposed are, give an undertaking in writing to make good any (unlikely) damage and explain that if anything goes wrong, surveyors can be called in to sort out the problem.

Whereas it was arguable under the London Building Acts (Amendment) Act 1939, the 1996 Act makes it clear that whenever a dispute arises under the Act, surveyors can settle a dispute. Since 'dispute' is not a term used to refer only to something which arises immediately after service of a notice, it is equally applicable if an argument arises – for example over damage or making good – after an initial consent has been given.

In many cases a letter, rather than an 'official' form, will be a more friendly form of notice, but it must contain the information required by the Act and, in the case of section 6, be accompanied by the necessary plans. Consent must also be written, which unfortunately tends to deter the nervous adjoining owner. That is why the personal approach is so important, since such owners can be reassured and have the whole thing explained to them. If for any reason you cannot see the adjoining owners face to face, a handwritten letter may be even more desirable in producing a friendly and informal response.

A good surveyor will advise a prospective appointing building owner/client when to adopt the personal approach, and when consent may reasonably be sought.

An adjoining owner who receives a notice should not automatically resort to the dispute procedures of the Act. Quite apart from the sheer neighbourliness of permitting next door to carry out the works without having to pay unnecessary surveyors' fees, today's adjoining owner may be tomorrow's building owner, and may be glad to have the same attitude shown to him. Having received a notice, therefore, or a visit from his neighbour, the adjoining owner should carefully consider how – or indeed whether – his property is likely to be affected.

If a garden (party fence) wall is to be rebuilt, and the adjoining owner is assured that any plants will be replaced, what risk is the adjoining owner at? I will tell you what risk. If he is too awkward, he may find section 11 (4) is invoked, and he is asked for his full proportion of the costs, as well as paying his own surveyor's fees.

In many cases the effect on an adjoining owner is very small indeed, and he should be perfectly happy to consent. He may feel that at least one professional should be involved, and in that case he can concur in the appointment of an agreed surveyor. This concurrence is the first possibility considered by the Act: both owners are happy that one surveyor can and will adequately hold the balance between the parties in the exercise of their rights and duties. If the adjoining owner is in doubt about the capability of the building owner's nominee, either technically or as to his impartiality, he can ask another surveyor whether he should consent, concur in an agreed surveyor or dissent.

A good surveyor will tell a prospective adjoining appointing owner/client when he can safely consent or concur and will therefore, as I pointed out earlier, in effect refuse instructions because it is in the best interests of the owner that he should do so.

CHAPTER 7

Appointing surveyors

The building owner's surveyor almost always wears two hats – not invariably, because just occasionally he is appointed after a 'dispute' has arisen, but usually. As an agent or adviser to his client, not only before service of notice but also during the progress of the works, he frequently has to advise on matters beyond the arbitral functions of the party wall surveyor.

Even before notice is served, the building owner's chosen adviser will be telling the owner who should be served and with what sort of notice. Very often the surveyor will draft and serve the notices himself, signing them on behalf of the building owner as his agent, if he has been duly authorized to do so. He will have a letter to that effect which will also say, as will the notice, that in the event of a dispute arising, the building owner 'would appoint' him as his surveyor under the Act. This form of words has been specifically approved by the courts, saying that it is a conditional appointment which comes into effect if the adjoining owner fails to consent, but does not do so if the latter agrees to the works.

It is a good idea if the prospective building owner's surveyor asks his appointing owner to sign a letter to use the wording given in *Figure 1*, the RICS guidance note, *Party Wall Legislation and Procedure* or The Pyramus and Thisbe Club's *Green Book*. Again, this makes a conditional appointment under the Act.

The building owner does not have to appoint a surveyor before serving notice. If he is happy, or indeed keen, to proceed by the agreed surveyor route, he can wait to see who the adjoining owner appoints and then, if satisfied with the appointee's credentials, accept him as 'agreed'. I know of a case where the building owner gave preliminary indications to his neighbours that he would in due course be serving formal notice, and all three of them said that they would be appointing the same surveyor. (Modesty forbids.) 'All right then' said the building owner, 'I will concur in his appointment'. However, I also know of another case in which an adjoining owner's surveyor refused to accept such concurrence on the grounds that his original appointing owner would not like it. I suppose that he was legally entitled to do so, but I think that he was very wrong to refuse, thus defeating the Act's aim of resolving any differences between owners as simply as possible.

It is highly desirable that the agreed surveyor system should become more widely understood, accepted and used, especially in small domestic jobs. It is quite wrong for the surveyors' fees to form a substantial part of the costs of a rear extension kitchen or living room, but if that extension touches both party walls, or if you are forming a room in the roof space, greedy surveyors on either side can make the job far too costly. Since the good party wall surveyor owes no particular allegiance to either side, it should be quite easy for a single agreed surveyor to make dispassionate decisions about perfectly straightforward construction matters. The cost of a single agreed surveyor should be less than a third of the likely costs of a surveyor on each side of the building owner's property plus one in the middle. The agreed surveyor should have far fewer arguments with himself than with the others, and so less of his single time will need to be charged.

In order for this welcome outcome to be achieved, surveyors must become practised at behaving as the Act envisages: as truly independent persons, serving truth, justice, the Act and the wall, and not the partisan interests of the owners. As they become more experienced, their reputation for impartial action should become wider and higher, and so increased use will be made of this method. Increased use will have a snowball effect and, with any luck, before long most domestic party wall jobs will be managed by a single agreed surveyor.

In more complex jobs, and certainly large commercial ones, it is probably better to have two surveyors, simply so that they can each have the benefit of the other's thoughts on the more difficult problems which are likely to arise. Some perfectly competent surveyors have expressed dismay at the prospect of being appointed as agreed surveyor on a major project. In principle, however, the single arbiter must be a desirable method of administering the Act.

A duly appointed building owner's surveyor always has to be clear about when he is advising a client and when he is a party wall surveyor. He must serve the Act, in the latter capacity, not the whims or desires of his appointing owner. When he is an agreed surveyor this is, if possible, even more true. It is for this reason that it is sometimes undesirable for the architect of a job to take on the party wall appointment, since it can be very difficult to differentiate between his two functions. However, in the interest of avoiding unnecessary costs to the building owner, when small works are being undertaken I think that economy should rule, and the architect should take special care to perform his party wall duties impartially. In major developments, it is almost always better for the two functions to be separated – even if the two people come from the same firm.

Adjoining owners are not moved by the same sense of urgency as building owners. If they dissent by inaction, the Act requires them to appoint a surveyor: the building owner cannot simply proceed *ex parte* on the grounds of apathy. He can try to persuade the adjoining owner to reconsider the matter and consent, or he can take steps to ensure the appointment of a surveyor.

The first step is to serve a notice in writing advising the adjoining owner that he must now choose a surveyor. If, after ten days, no appointment has been made, the building owner (or his surveyor, if so authorized – and if he is in receipt of one of the approved letters, he will be) can either press the adjoining owner for action, or appoint a surveyor himself. (I have dealt earlier with the appointment of a surveyor by a willing adjoining owner, so here I am only considering the dilatory or obstructive type.)

Frequently, action by one party induces sudden activity by the hitherto dormant other party (as we shall see when dealing with *ex parte* awards later – see chapter thirteen). If you can, therefore, it is often a good idea to explain to the surveyor who is being appointed by the building owner on behalf of the adjoining owner just what is happening, and to enquire whether he would be willing to withdraw if the adjoining owner belatedly makes his own appointment. Legally, the earlier appointment would stand, and if the adjoining owner has not acted within ten days his subsequent appointment would be invalid, but it can make for a much happier relationship if the latecomer is allowed to act: this can only happen if the first appointee voluntarily withdraws.

When making an appointment on another owner's behalf, great care should be taken to choose a suitable surveyor. He should not be someone whom you might hope to push around, but someone you would be happy to have acting for you. It is of course quite proper to appoint someone who is already involved in the works, perhaps on behalf of another adjoining owner. I did a fairly large development where I was the agreed surveyor in a number of cases, and almost all the others appointed the same surveyor to act for all those who had failed themselves to make any such appointment.

However you go about it, when the adjoining owner dissents, by positive action or inaction, a second surveyor must be appointed. It is not lawful simply to proceed.

Note: the building owner cannot, nor can his surveyor, appoint the first surveyor as an agreed one.

CHAPTER 8

Selecting the third surveyor

It is the duty of the first two surveyors, immediately after their appointment, to select a third surveyor. Some people have asked why the first two are 'appointed' and the third 'selected'. It is because – if it matters – the owners appoint someone of their choice, while the surveyors select from a comparatively small number of suitably qualified candidates.

The reason for instant selection is that, with no matters yet in dispute, the choice of an umpire should be made without difficulty. Despite the fact that good party wall surveyors should never fall out with their opposite numbers, even though they may disagree with them on interpretation or on how certain works should best be carried out, it is a sad fact of life that less than good party wall surveyors are sometimes appointed. Such surveyors see their role as advocates for the owner who appointed them (whom they think of as a client) or else regard any different view from their own as a personal affront. Since you cannot have them thrown off the case for stupidity or incompetence, it is as well to agree on a third surveyor with them before anything has happened to offend them.

Unfortunately, it is the worst sort of client-regarding surveyor with whom it is most difficult to agree upon an arbiter. Some will not have anyone from The Pyramus and Thisbe Club. ('You're all friends with each other and you always confirm each other's views' – even when all three of you are members, and two of you disagree?). Some, with more justification, will only agree on a few prominent members of the Club. Fortunately, a mechanism is provided by section 10 (8) of the Act by which a third surveyor may be nominated by the local authority, if the first two cannot agree. However, it is very rare for this kind of struggle to occur, so let us consider the more usual friendly sequence.

The building owner's surveyor, as soon as he knows who the adjoining owner's surveyor is, usually submits a list of three names. The recipient chooses one (or crosses out two) and the job is done. Sometimes the adjoining owner's surveyor will genuinely be unhappy with the list submitted, and will send back his own three suggestions, one of whom is likely to be acceptable. If none of this works, you must use the procedures of section 10 (8).

It is not enough to say that if a dispute arises, the surveyors will choose a third surveyor, or even that they will delegate the selection to the President of the RICS or the RIBA, or the appointing officer of the local authority. They must choose someone specific, now. If, later, that someone declines to act and the first two surveyors cannot agree on a substitute, then their chosen alternative method can come into play, because it is not improper to choose someone other than the local authority to make the selection. The use of that body's appointing officer is the default system.

So who should you choose? There are, of course, a number of members of The Pyramus and Thisbe Club who can safely be chosen. That they are members indicates that at least they are seriously interested in the subject of party walls and, what is more, they have access to other experienced members if they think that additional opinions or advice would assist them. However, you may not know any members, or there may be none in the area where the job is – though that is becoming increasingly unlikely as the Club has expanded to all parts of the country. The qualities which a good third surveyor must have are a good legal understanding of the Act (or an ability to understand it, if it is new to him) and a good practical knowledge of building construction, so that he can decide between different approaches to a particular problem. The more experience he has of the Act, the better.

Everyone has someone to whom they can turn for advice to discuss knotty problems, however great an authority they themselves may be – or think themselves to be. That is the person whom you should suggest as third surveyor to your opposite number, and if you are lucky enough to have three gurus on your consulting list, you can even offer an adequate range of choice.

In something like three thousand party wall jobs I have only had recourse to the appointing officer on two or three occasions, so it is a pretty rare occurrence. Given the good will – or at any rate lack of ill will – which, as I have already said, should exist at the outset of a job, you ought to have little difficulty in finding a name acceptable to both surveyors.

CHAPTER 9

The schedule of condition

Having served notice on the adjoining owner and dealt with the appointment of surveyors, it is time to start getting to grips with the actual job. One of the first things that you are likely to have to do is to take a schedule of condition. In order to do this, it is first necessary to gain entry to the premises to be described. This is not always straight-forward. In certain town centres the activities which take place next door to perfectly respectable properties are not always such that their practi-tioners – or their owners, if they can be identified – are keen to have their premises invaded, even by harmless party wall surveyors. In some large blocks of metropolitan flats the long leasehold owners are foreign companies or individuals who are rarely in the country, and by the time you have contacted them to arrange an appointment for inspection, they are on their way out again.

Although the Act provides methods of dealing with both of these prob-lems, it does not make it easy to gain entry. There are two criminal offences covered by the Act. (There were three in the 1939 Act, and the loss of the third is so sad for the practitioners of that Act that I will not upset those who know not what they have lost by telling them about it.) If someone who knows, or ought to know, that a building owner, his contractor or his surveyor has a right to enter the next door premises, wilfully refuses entry (offence no.1) or obstructs someone once they are in (offence no.2) they can be convicted in the magistrates court. The 'ought to know' bit is to protect a weekly tenant or a cleaner who quite rightly is reluctant to admit some stranger to his or his employer's house. As long as you can find someone to deal with, you can obtain entry by giving the requisite fourteen days' notice under section 8, and using the threat of proceedings under section 16 in the face of recalcitrance.

The answer to the problem of finding nobody is, in the phrase that has become well known, 'to break down the door with a policeman'. In other words, if all other attempts have failed and the premises are closed you may, if accompanied by a police officer, force open gates or doors as necessary. Personally I have never done this, although my assistants have done it in my name on a few occasions – almost invariably at seedy Soho premises. Somehow, one does not have quite the same insouciant attitude to valuable West End flat doors.

It is my opinion that if you have made all reasonable efforts to obtain admission in order to take a schedule and have been thwarted by the actions – or inactions – of the adjoining owner, the burden of proof in any subsequent discussions about liability for damage has probably changed. Whereas the building owner is normally held to be liable for any otherwise inexplicable damage which occurs during his works, if a hitherto invisible adjoining owner suddenly surfaces with a claim for damage, it will be up to him to prove that it is the result of the building owner's actions.

So far in this chapter there has been a great deal of cart but not a lot of horse. Let us therefore get to our muttons – to mix both metaphor and livestock. What is the purpose of a schedule of condition? How should it be taken? What should it record? Let us consider each of these three questions separately.

What is the purpose of a schedule of condition?

The purpose of a schedule of condition is to record the present state of repair of a building, structure or premises (including gardens and the like) before works are carried out. Then, any damage caused by those works may be readily identified. The schedule protects adjoining owners against building owners and, especially, their contractors who refuse to admit that anything is their fault unless presented with incontrovertible proof of that fact. It also protects the building owners against adjoining owners who only notice age-old defects when they hear the noise of work next door, and promptly blame the building owner for every crack and stain in sight regardless of how long it has been there.

How should it be taken?

Knowing the purpose of a schedule should make it easier to answer the next two questions. Photographs or video films will very rarely identify adequately the sort of crack which will be debatable between two sensible surveyors. They are helpful to identify the area which is being described in a schedule, but are no substitute for the written or dictated word.

Some people like to record the schedule on a pocket tape recorder; some like to do it long hand; and some even take their secretary on site with them and dictate it on the spot. (I usually suspect an ulterior motive in such cases.) This element does not matter, however, as long as the schedule makes it perfectly clear what it is dealing with. I have been confronted with schedules from which I have been unable to decide which building is involved, let alone which room or which floor.

This leads to a further question: whether schedules are better taken jointly, or taken by one surveyor and later checked by the other. In my youth I favoured the former, but am now totally convinced that the latter is the more efficient. If one surveyor is a passionate Newcastle supporter and the other Sunderland (or Harlequins and Saracens) they may easily miss a vital piece of information while engaged in enthusiastic debate. The two times added together, furthermore, are likely to be less than that of a joint visit.

Schedules are ideal work for juniors. A one-man practice will have to do everything connected with a job, however lowly, but more stratified practices should make a habit of giving easy work to the less experienced members of the team, and reserving the highly experienced – and more expensive – surveyors for the trickier bits. Interpretation of the Act may be best left to a partner, but anyone who can tell a beetle flight hole from the imprint of a drawing pin (and I once – for a short time – had a prize-winning assistant who could not) should be capable of taking an adequate schedule, once instructed in the art. This should be reflected in the fees for a job, and a one-man band should not charge his high-powered thinking rate for schedule taking. I will say more about this when dealing with fees (see chapter fifteen).

What should it record?

This leaves the question of what a schedule should contain. Since its purpose is to forestall argument as to damage, there is no need to record anything that is unlikely to be damaged. You do not need elaborate descriptions of the colour scheme, the pattern of the carpets or the number of light fittings. You should carefully specify what you have been unable to inspect because of locked doors, heavy wardrobes against the wall or panelling. If a window is cracked, or the glass in a picture or mirror hanging on a party wall, that should certainly be recorded, and it may be necessary to advise moving such objects from vulnerable positions while the works are going on. (I once had a painting by Guardi moved in a Kensington flat, and the widow of a theatrical knight had two very valuable mirrors temporarily removed.)

Cracks, however, are the most sensitive items and, in my opinion, need the most careful record. Both the length of crack and its width need to be accurately detailed: the use of a crack gauge, such as the one sold by The Pyramus and Thisbe Club, can be very helpful. If the walls are likely to be redecorated, the end of a crack can be physically marked, and pencil can usually be removed anyway. A coin can form a simple gauge, by drawing round it across a crack, since any break in the circle will be obvious – as long as you do not use a twenty or fifty pence piece. A two pence piece is ideal.

You have to make an empirical decision as to how far from the party wall (or nearest wall to the works, in the case of section 6 of the Act) your schedule should extend. The first natural break, such as a door or window, is a useful guide, or about six feet or so. (I think this may be the first time that my unreformed imperialism has surfaced in this manual, but I refuse to use a purely arbitrary system of measurement, instead of one based on human dimensions.) You must use your judgement, but whatever you do you will get it wrong sometimes. I have had two cases where the whole of next door's building tilted, so that all the damage took place at the junction with next door but one.

The building owner's surveyor will usually take the initial schedule and send it to the adjoining owner's surveyor to be checked and agreed. The first surveyor will naturally hope to have noticed and included every crack or other defect, such as staining, spalling or crazing, but it is every bit as much the job of the adjoining owner's surveyor to make good any omissions as to strike out any incorrect inclusions – such as a cobweb mistaken for cracking. I hope that I am not addressing any surveyor who would notice an omitted crack and think: 'Aha, I can claim for that later'.

The aim of both surveyors should be to produce a document which, when the works next door are finished, will prove easy to read against a building which they may not have seen for six months or more. It should also be so complete that there can be no argument between them as to whether damage is new or not, although inevitably there will be times when the cause of the damage may not be obvious. As in all things under the Act, the idea of the schedule of condition is to resolve any disputes cheaply and simply.

CHAPTER 10

Communications

In party wall matters, the routes of communication are very important in theory, but in practice sometimes have to be short-circuited. A 'surveyor' has no power to order anyone to do anything, except his appointing owner, but in effect he often has to ensure that the architect, engineer or contractor is ordered to do something. He can therefore speed up the process by advising the person in question that he is going to ask the building owner (usually; more rarely the adjoining owner) to ask that person to do something. The sensible architect (etc.) will then do it.

For example, an adjoining owner's surveyor may request a drawing showing some detail. The building owner's surveyor may agree that he ought to have it. Technically, the way to ensure this happens is for the surveyors to award that it should be produced, but this is never done in practice. The building owner's surveyor asks the building owner, who asks the engineer (etc.) and it comes. Even this is often circumvented by a direct request: sometimes even from the engineer advising the adjoining owner's surveyor straight to the building owner's engineer.

Perhaps this is a good moment to mention the duties of the adjoining owner's surveyor's engineer. That is what he is: an engineer providing necessary advice on matters too abstruse for even a competent party wall surveyor to check from his own knowledge. The engineer is not there to redesign the building owner's engineer's work, nor to check every calculation or every nut and bolt. He should run his eye over the scheme, perhaps check one or two important calculations and advise his surveyor whether the proposals seem adequate, or whether more detail is required. As I have just said, it is sometimes quicker and more efficient for him to communicate directly with the other engineer, but this is an unofficial – though often beneficial – route. Some engineers fear that they will be liable to the adjoining owner unless they check everything. In the first place, that is not what they are being employed to do, and secondly, as leading cases make clear, the building owner will remain responsible for the consequences of his actions, whether the other side have approved his proposals or not.

I must stress, however, that the engagement of an engineer is an unusual step, and should not be needed in most normal jobs tackled by a competent building surveyor.

A prudent party wall surveyor secures the approval of his opposite number before engaging the services of an engineer because the engineer's fees will need to be included in the award. If the building owner's surveyor is suddenly confronted with a demand for these, without forewarning, he may very well refuse to award them, which could present the adjoining owner's surveyor or his owner with a nasty bill.

It might also be said that the owners only communicate with their surveyors once, when they appoint them, and the surveyors only communicate with the owners twice, when they accept the appointment and when they publish their award. In reality, letters and phone calls flow much more freely, particularly if unexpected crises arise. For example, if the adjoining owner cannot get hold of his surveyor and rings the building owner's surveyor to get the water turned off/hole repaired/concrete removed. Sometimes quite good relations can prevail between an adjoining owner and a building owner's surveyor – which is how I came to be driven down the wrong side of the Vauxhall Bridge Road in excess of the speed limit by Stirling Moss.

However, the legal position should not be lost sight of. The Act envisages surveyor-to-surveyor communication, followed by an award which is published to the parties involved. Thereafter, if the building owner produces new details, or the adjoining owner suffers new damage, they communicate these matters to their respective surveyors who tell each other, and decide what to do about it. Having decided, they communicate this decision to the owners. Strictly speaking, I think that any such decision is an award, and perhaps should sometimes be given in formal fashion. More often, day-to-day matters are settled by exchanges of letters.

While you should never forget the official channels, informal communication is often the best method. Many an ugly scene has been averted because the building owner's surveyor responded quickly and directly to an anguished telephone call from the adjoining owner and reacted by telling the contractor direct to take the necessary action. It may not be totally correct legally, but it is sometimes the right and practical way to go about things.

CHAPTER 11

Change of ownership

The Act says that the building owner must give notice of his intentions to the adjoining owner. When this happens at the outset of a job, everything is straightforward. But what happens when the identity of the 'owner' – either side of the wall – changes, or the building owner's proposals change because of site conditions or for other reasons? The answers are different in law and in practice.

The easiest matter to deal with is a change of adjoining owner. The original owner is bound by the original notice, and must advise any incoming purchaser or tenant of that notice and its effect to date. The new owner will be bound by anything which has been formally concluded so far: the notice received; a surveyor appointed; a schedule of condition agreed; an award made. Sometimes the outgoing owner neglects or forgets to inform the new owners, who are very surprised when someone turns up and tells them that he is their appointed surveyor. They may be surprised, but there is nothing they can do about it under the Act, though they may possibly have some rights against their forgetful seller/lessor.

Of course, if the new owners redecorate everything it can make the schedule rather difficult to check. The two surveyors just have to do the best they can, because the neglectful departing one will probably not have remembered to tell them either.

Changes on the building owner's side are much more difficult to deal with, and there isn't universal agreement on the situation, although I believe that the leading cases and the majority support my view. Since 'the building owner' must give notice, then new building owner equals new notice. In other words, he cannot take the benefit of his predecessor's notice, but must give notice himself. This is true even if ownership changes during the progress of a job, so that work might have to stop for two months (at least to the party wall) while notice ran. In practice, this very rarely happens because anyone who is suffering the disruption that goes with any building works next door will not want that agony unnecessarily prolonged, and will therefore agree to waive the two month waiting period. Note that only the owner can do this, not his surveyor.

What usually happens is that the adjoining owner's surveyor advises his owner to accept the notice and allow work to proceed without interruption, and promptly draws up a new award in which an additional fee is charged for this service. The most likely thing to hold up proceedings is if the adjoining owner has any reason to distrust the new building owner, either from lack of knowledge of him – or the reverse – and therefore wants security for expenses which he did not require from the previous owner.

At the same time, it should be noted that the outgoing building owner cannot shrug off any responsibilities or liabilities which he has undertaken during the currency of his notice. He can get an indemnity from the incoming owner, but *vis-à-vis* the adjoining owner he is still liable.

Changes of plan produce much the same results, both theoretically and in fact – if not more so. As I explained when dealing with the service of notices in general (see chapter four), changes often occur in foundation details, especially pile depths, which are nodded through by surveyors. The same is true with other changes of a structural nature, which inevitably occur during many jobs. Very often the prime award will give the surveyors the right to decide any minor variations, and section 7 (5) of the Act says that no deviation is permitted from agreed (or awarded) proposals unless subsequently agreed by the owners or surveyors acting on their behalf.

I do not think, however, that the courts would support a change in the nature of the works which had merely been agreed by the surveyors and had not been the subject of a new notice. This section of the Act speaks of 'deviation', which implies a change of detail rather than fundamental alteration. Changes of depth of pile, width of underpinning bay and height of wall are all probably deviations. Taking down a party wall not previously destined to be rebuilt, or not underpinning where it was previously proposed, might be deemed more than deviation.

In practice, however, the same results are usually obtained as in the case of new owners. Both sides, advised by their surveyors, would rather see the work brought to a successful conclusion without unnecessary interruption and will therefore allow it to proceed without the delays caused by the service of new notices.

To sum up then: a new adjoining owner changes nothing; a new building owner or a new scheme can bring everything to a halt, theoretically. In fact, changes of ownership are usually smoothly incorporated in the awards of the surveyors.

CHAPTER 12

The extent of a surveyor's authority

Party wall surveyors are often called upon to exceed their authority. They must resist such requests, at least with their party wall hat on. Their powers are limited to dealing with the matters which are covered by the notices and by the Act. The 'building owner's surveyor' (whom I put in quotation marks because he is not that in this sentence) often has to advise his owner on matters outside his party wall powers. The 'adjoining owner's surveyor' (ditto) is often asked to deal with crane swinging or rights of light. There is nothing to stop either person from performing these extraneous functions, but they must remember that they are not doing so as statutory party wall surveyors.

It would be quite wrong to try to settle matters such as I have just mentioned in the party wall award or to lay down the position of the boundary therein. Although the modern legal practice is to try to preserve whatever is correct in an award, rather than to throw it all out because of a minor illegality, it is obviously better to avoid making *ultra vires* awards which might be so far off the beam as to be totally rejected.

Make it clear when you are acting as party wall surveyor, and when as agent. Although you must not put into the award anything not covered by the Act, you can have an exchange of letters – preferably between the owners themselves – to record any agreement on other matters. It is not a bad idea to have two separate people in the same office dealing with the different aspects of a job, one dealing with matters inside the Act, and the other dealing with matters outside, such as crane swinging, to ensure that this dichotomy is observed.

You must also ensure, even in performing your undoubted party wall functions, that you do not go too far – physically. You can control noisy working on the party wall: you cannot control it on the whole site. You can stipulate what work can be done to the party wall: you cannot dictate what is done to the front elevation. You can insist that any dirt or debris is cleared daily from the adjoining owner's premises: you cannot demand that the whole site is kept in a state of cleanliness.

In matters where you are given authority by the Act or by the award, your powers are considerable. You can dictate to the owners that they should allow other people on to their property, or even that they should allow the external wall of their building – as they see it – to be demolished. You can only do this formally, however, in an award which could be appealed to the courts by an unhappy owner. If you stick to your powers under the Act, the appeal is likely to be unsuccessful. Know your powers then, but know your limitations even better. The powers are so wide that they must be used properly.

CHAPTER 13

The award

I have talked quite a lot about party wall awards without actually dealing properly with them. Now we get to that. The award is the end product of the surveyors' negotiations and may be produced by one, two or three surveyors (though the last is the least common and the first quite rare). In the normal course of events, the building owner's surveyor and the adjoining owner's surveyor jointly produce an award setting out all the details of the proposed works and the conditions upon which the building owner may execute those works. Let us look at the most usual sort of award first, before considering the rarer kinds.

The usual award starts with a recital of people and events. The building owner, his address, and his surveyor are named; the same is done for the adjoining owner. The date and the nature of the originating notice are stated. This is important, because without notice, there are no party wall proceedings, and the notice must give particulars of the proposed works. The award can only deal with the works set out in that notice. As we have already seen, 'deviations' from the detail of the proposed works are permitted, but going outside the nature of the notice is not.

The third surveyor is named in the award. Even if he has not been formally selected sooner – and he should have been – the appearance of his name in a signed award must constitute formal agreement upon him. Very often the method of selecting an alternative, should the chosen one be unable or unwilling to act, is set out in the award. Although there is a default mechanism in the Act, I think – though there are those who disagree with me – that it is perfectly proper for the two surveyors, if they are both members of the same professional body – or even if they are not, for that matter – to agree that a substitute should be chosen, if they are unable to agree upon one, by the President of that body, or by the Chairman of The Pyramus and Thisbe Club for example.

Then the award really gets down to business and sets out the works, probably in more detail but covering the same ground, described in the notice. This is what the building owner wants to do, and you must be careful to express it accurately. Do not, accidentally or otherwise, attempt to bind the building owner to rebuilding a six storey warehouse with fifty foot piles: his aspirations may change – or his finances.

In the next section you do most certainly bind the building owner. He is only permitted to execute his proposals if he properly protects the neighbour's life, limb and property; if he keeps the noise down; if he clears up after him; and so on. Do not forget that under the Act the building owner may have a perfect right to go on to the adjoining owner's property in order to carry out some of his works. It must be clear within what limits that right is to be exercised. Hours of noisy work may need to be specified, and these must vary according to the nature of the adjoining premises. Offices will have no objection to weekend working, while domestic properties most certainly will. If the surveyors cannot agree, sometimes the environmental health officer will be called in by an indignant adjoining owner, but in my experience the authorities tend to be more generous in allowing hours of working to the building owner than adjoining owner's surveyors incline to be.

Sometimes the circumstances suggest or compel unusual results. An example of the first is a case where works adjoined an impresario who needed to speak to New York most days, and it was agreed to suspend work during the most important one and a half hour overlap of office hours. In an example of the second kind, work was being done above an open stretch of 'underground' railway, and could only be carried out during the very few hours of the night when the trains were not running. When the workmen made rather too much noise there were complaints, but it is hard to see how else the work could have been completed without great disruption to London's transport system.

The rights of the surveyors for access to inspect the works should be awarded. The building owner's surveyor normally has to give reasonable notice to visit the adjoining owner's property, but the adjoining owner's surveyor usually has an unfettered right to descend upon the building site at any time to ensure that the conditions mentioned above are being complied with, and that no unauthorized works are taking place. (It is important, by the way, that the site foreman should understand this, since he might be summonsed under section 16 of the Act for refusing or obstructing entry.)

Several other clauses are often added, saying that works should comply with planning consents and building regulations, but in my opinion these are not strictly speaking part of the party wall surveyors' concerns. It is also customary to exclude any question of rights of light, even though section 9 does this anyway, just to allay the fears of lay readers of an award.

Finally, the award usually records that the building owner should pay the fees of the adjoining owner's surveyor, and frequently settles the sum of those fees (see chapter fifteen for more details). It is bad, wrong, and unprofessional to refuse to sign an award solely because fees cannot be agreed. The proper course of action is to say so in the award, and leave them to be settled by further discussion or by the third surveyor. Very occasionally each party pays their own surveyor, such as when both sides are carrying out work simultaneously, but the above is the usual practice.

The building owner's surveyor usually prepares the fair copies, signs them, does not date them, and sends one unsigned and two signed copies to the adjoining owner's surveyor. The latter countersigns and dates both (keeps the unsigned one), sends one to his appointing owner and the other back to his opposite number who forwards it to his owner. It is customary for signatures to be witnessed, but the Act does not actually say that they have to be. It is better to do so, however, and if you have witnesses who are not partners in the firm, make sure that they give their home address, since they are not entitled to use the firm's address as their own.

The signed copies must be forthwith sent to the appointing owners by their respective surveyors. It is important that this should be done at once so that the owner may have the opportunity to appeal within fourteen days if he is really dissatisfied with something in the award.

What happens to the award after it leaves you is not strictly speaking your concern, but its validity comes to an end when the works are over and the schedule checked, though its helpfulness may last rather longer. It often enables the erstwhile adjoining owner now turned building owner to plan his proposed works more efficiently when he can see what went on next door.

Now let us turn to the other types of award. If the first two surveyors cannot agree on anything, they can ask the third surveyor to make the whole award, but usually their disagreement is confined to a few elements only. They should then ask the third surveyor to award on those limited points only. He can choose whether to try to get both of them to agree with him, so that all three sign the award (very rare indeed); he can join with one of the others in signing, if the latter is clearly right and facing someone who just does not – or will not – understand the law (not very common); or he can make the award himself, after listening to representations from the first two. I will deal separately with the third surveyor proceedings shortly (see chapter fourteen).

If one surveyor refuses to act, or fails to act for ten days after being required to do so, the first surveyor can proceed *ex parte*, that is to say on his own, and his acts are in effect those of an agreed surveyor. This power, however, is limited to the matters on which an answer has been requested, so unless he has asked his opposite number to agree an award, he cannot make that award *ex parte*. Such actions are not frequent, but by no means unknown. What usually follows is that the other person at last wakes up, and promptly denies that the first surveyor was entitled to proceed *ex parte*. If this produces an agreed award, well and good, but do not let such people lure you into withdrawing a perfectly valid award, while they again go into hibernation. You should be prepared to accept a jointly agreed award as successor to your *ex parte* one, but not as a substitute.

Even an agreed surveyor must produce an award. He cannot just let work proceed 'as long as he is happy with it'. Both owners are entitled to know what the surveyor has decided in relation to construction details, or safeguarding foundations, and the delivery of the award is their opportunity to challenge the surveyor's decisions.

The award is binding on both owners, and they must appeal against it within fourteen days or it becomes unchallengeable. (In fact, the courts will accept out of time appeals if they can find any legal justification for doing so, on the grounds that an invalid award does not qualify for the protection of the fourteen day clause. However, it is hard to see why an award should be appealed except because it has some illegality or irregularity in it: it is hardly likely to be on the technical aspects, but this appears to be all that is covered by sections 10 (16) and (17).)

Although an award cannot be registered, it should be carefully retained as a pseudo-legal document. It is, strictly speaking, *functus officio* as soon as the works and any making good are completed, but it may come in handy when future works are contemplated. It is helpful, therefore, to provide the award with a stiff cover, to assist its longevity. And a smartly produced award does the surveyors' reputation no harm.

CHAPTER 14

Third surveyors and appeals

A reference to the third surveyor can be as informal as you like. Very often, one surveyor will ring up, explain that both he and his opposite number will accept the third surveyor's opinion, and ask for interpretation of a clause in the Act. Ten minutes on the telephone, and that is it – no fee and no fuss. Sometimes the dispute will be much more complicated, and virtually a full arbitration hearing will be needed to arrive at a solution.

It is really up to the third surveyor himself to decide how to proceed. Sometimes he will want to see the site before deciding anything, and sometimes he will not want to see it at all. I have developed a fairly standard practice for major matters. I see the two surveyors in my office in order to thrash out clearly – and in comfort – what the issues are. Then I make an accompanied site visit, after which we may have a further discussion. When I am sure that the issues are clear, and that there are no other matters waiting in the wings to be raised just when I thought that everything was settled, I invite each surveyor to send me two copies of his submission, setting out what he would like me to award. When I have both submissions, I send off the second copy to the other side, and invite a riposte in similar fashion. This ensures that the speedier surveyor is not disadvantaged by the other chap reading his submission before writing his own. Occasionally the parties will seek to have a third go, and if I feel that the ripostes bring up new matters I will allow this.

Being in possession of all the arguments, I then toss a coin. Well, no I don't, but I have had cases where I felt that I was as likely to get it right by that method as by days of anguished consideration. Reluctantly, I have always chosen the latter route, and then I draft my award, usually with all the same preambles about notice, owners, addresses, etc., which will be useful if that award alone survives for the future. I decide all the matters that have been submitted to me, and have the award typed but not signed. Then I write to the two surveyors to tell them that my award is ready and may be taken up on payment of my fees.

I do not say in my letter which side will eventually bear my fees since that would reveal, in effect, my award. The award sets out who is to pay, but in the meantime one party is usually more anxious than the other to get their hands on the award, and so they pay the fees in full. I then sign the award and post a copy to each surveyor.

Occasionally, I may have comments to make, either because I think that the surveyors need help or because I believe that they have acted wrongly. Such remarks are not suitable for inclusion in an award, so I send a side letter with the award, which forms no part of any formal decision.

It is only very rarely that an award by the first two surveyors is appealed. After all, the party's own surveyor will have agreed to it, and will not be encouraging his owner to dispute his views. More often it is a third surveyor's award which will prove unpalatable to one owner, supported in all probability by his surveyor whose views have not been upheld.

The single most important question arising from an appeal is whether the award is binding in the meanwhile. Although opinion is divided on the answer, I incline to the view that until the award has been set aside, it is still in effect, and that it would be contrary to the ethos of the legislation to allow an appeal to frustrate a properly obtained award. It is also my opinion that a surveyor should only encourage his owner to appeal if he is convinced that an award is utterly wrong, and not just because his feelings are hurt by the third surveyor disagreeing with him.

An appeal is like any other court proceedings. It will almost invariably be to the county court, and will take a comparatively long time. As section 10 (17) of the Act makes clear, the court has the power to completely review the whole award, and it has been held that the court may receive evidence not forming part of the original award proceedings.

As I have said, an appeal is usually against a third surveyor's award, but he is not the respondent. 'It's as if I were asked to justify my judgment to the Court of Appeal', said a judge to whom this proposition was once put. (I was the third surveyor and had been summoned to attend, which I did, but promptly asked the court to dismiss me from the proceedings, which it did.) Suppose that the adjoining owner appeals, then although the building owner is also not, strictly speaking and in my opinion, the respondent to the proceedings, he is usually treated as such, and is very often happy to be so. It would be interesting to see what happened if the non-appealing owner chose not to take an interest. I do not think that he should then be made liable for costs, if he had not opposed the proceedings, but a solicitor friend tells me that, since he could have avoided the necessity for an appeal by agreeing with the appellant, it is extremely unlikely that costs would not be awarded against the 'respondent'.

Appeals are an undesirable interruption to the smooth flow of party wall proceedings. They should not be encouraged, and all three surveyors should strive to make their awards so sound as to be appeal proof. There is, unfortunately, no discouraging the vexatious litigant type.

CHAPTER 15

Fees and expenses

Fees are paid to surveyors: expenses to owners. Let us deal with fees first, when it will be necessary to differentiate between fees payable to the adjoining owner's surveyor and those due to the building owner's surveyor.

Fees

At section 10 (13) the Act says that the costs of the award and associated matters shall be paid by the decision of the surveyors. They almost invariably decide that the building owner shall pay. A more difficult question is: how many people should he pay? It is much simpler if the answer is: only the adjoining owner's surveyor. Even when the latter has received additional advice from others, they are in fact advising him, and are not persons for whose fees the owner is directly responsible. This also helps to make it clear that, for example, an engineer advising the adjoining owner's surveyor is not designing the structure nor responsible for its soundness: he is merely telling his side whether it smells all right.

When such additional fees are likely to be incurred, the adjoining owner's surveyor should ask his opposite number if such charges will be acceptable, giving the building owner's surveyor an opportunity to dispute the need for outside assistance.

Very, very rarely should solicitors' fees be payable under the Act. If an adjoining owner rushes off to a solicitor when he receives a notice, instead of to a surveyor, the solicitor's fee for reading the Act, discovering that his client should have gone to a surveyor, and then recommending one, is not part of 'the reasonable costs ... (of) ... making or obtaining an award'. If, on the other hand, the services of a solicitor have been necessary in making a building owner comply with the Act in serving notice, then the fees are reasonably incurred in obtaining an award.

How much? That is the big question. How much can an adjoining

59

owner's surveyor reasonably charge? Obviously, one cannot quote rates, since they change with time and place, but one can offer guidance.

By the time an award is being drafted, the adjoining owner's surveyor has a good knowledge of the scope of the works and what is required of him. He can estimate how many visits will be needed up to the end of the job, including one to check the schedule, and so he can put a figure on the number of hours needed for the whole job. If he agrees that and his rate with the building owner's surveyor, then all is settled.

Many referrals to me as third surveyor have been on the subject of fees, and very often the surveyor has spent a large amount of time in the preliminary stages: one hour for receiving notices and considering them; one and a half hours to visit the 'client' and explain the notice to them; and so on. Fifteen minutes is all it should take to check whether a notice is valid and what it is about; and most of the time one does not need to go to see one's appointing owner to explain.

Where surveyors are sole practitioners they cannot get assistants to do the donkey work, but I do think that they should charge less for doing it themselves. Finally, although I know that it is a bit much to ask, a conscientious surveyor should have some regard to the size of a job in his charging. The Act is not a licence for surveyors to print money, and if a small householder is building a rear extension, he should not expect to pay out half as much again in fees to rapacious adjoining, or indeed building, owners' surveyors.

Strictly speaking, I suppose that an award could determine the building owner's surveyor's fees, and I have known this to be done once or twice when the building owner was being difficult about paying. The award provided the surveyor with a good legal basis for his claim. However, as explained earlier, the building owner's surveyor does a mixture of work in that capacity and as agent and general adviser. Sorting out the 'awardable' fees from the 'chargeable' fees would probably add considerably to the bill, and it is therefore customary for that surveyor to send in an account for all the time he has spent on the job, in accordance with the rates which he will have agreed with the building owner at the outset.

Expenses

Expenses are a different matter altogether. We have already dealt with security for expenses (see chapter five), so we must now deal with other sorts. The general preamble to section 11 of the Act states that unless otherwise specified, the building owner is responsible for the costs of work, but several other sections also lay down how costs are to be borne. Section 1 (3), for example, provides that the cost of constructing a new party wall or party fence wall is to be shared according to use, while other clauses specifically place the costs on the building owner.

The most complicated provision is found in sections 11 (4) and (5), where it is enacted that when a wall is rebuilt because it is defective, the costs are to be shared, regard being had to use of and also to responsibility for the defect. This can be a difficult equation, but the surveyors must tackle it with care and if, for example, one side uses the wall to enclose a building, but has kept its side in pretty good repair, while the other only uses the wall as a boundary wall, and has woefully neglected it, you might have 80 per cent of one against 90 per cent of the other.

When an adjoining owner makes additional use of an existing party wall by enclosing, or enclosing further, upon it, or when he requires a building owner to maintain the height of a wall which the building owner would like to reduce, he can be required to pay the appropriate modern sum for this use. Say he encloses on an additional 10 square yards (8 square metres) of brickwork: he must pay half the cost in today's values of building those 10 square yards. There is considerable argument about foundation costs in those circumstances. However, it would seem from the words of section 11 (11) that if the first raising necessitated underpinning the wall, the cost of that is part of 'the expenses incurred by the building owner in carrying out that work', and therefore the second user of the wall will have to pay his share of that, as well as of the raised brickwork.

Contrariwise, it seems to me that if the first owner can successfully raise the wall without having to underpin, but the load proposed by the second owner will be the last straw which breaks the foundations' back, the latter has to bear the whole cost of the underpinning and the proportion of the raised brickwork: he cannot set off half the foundation costs against those of the upper wall. This may seem a little hard on the second owner, but I think that this is what the Act decides.

CHAPTER 16

The progress of the works

As a party wall surveyor, the building owner's appointee has very little to do off his own bat once the award has been published. (As the adviser to his client, he may have quite a lot to do.) He will largely be reactive to any comments or complaints from the other side. Strictly speaking, those last two words refer to the other surveyor, but it often happens that urgent action is needed, the adjoining owner's surveyor is not available, and the owner rings the building owner's surveyor direct. In such cases it is absurd to stand upon protocol: if the owner has a justified complaint, it is quicker – and cheaper – for the building owner's surveyor to act on it at once.

The adjoining owner's surveyor will have allowed for a certain number of 'progress' visits in his agreed fee, and will check that the works are being carried out in accordance with the award – so far as the party wall is concerned. It is not for him to complain if the rest of the site has changed its nature completely. He will also check whether damage has occurred and whether his owner's site is being kept clean. Quite often, however, he will be called to site by his owner, alleging serious damage or wrongful acts of omission or commission. Sometimes, these allegations may have some justification. The award will also have allowed for additional fees to be paid if damage occurs and needs sorting out, and then there may be a further award doing just that and settling those fees. If the calls to site are unjustified, and cannot be included within the expected visits, it is my opinion that fees for them should be charged to the adjoining owner. I cannot say, however, that I am aware of this happening as standard practice – or even at all.

The most difficult things to deal with during the progress of the works, in my experience, are noise and dirt. As I have already explained, the surveyor's powers only extend to the party wall and its immediate vicinity (or the nature of the work under section 6 of the Act). Dust and noise can very rarely be so precisely limited. Direct work to the party wall itself can of course be controlled, but lay neighbours are often deceived by structure-borne noise, which can be caused by work taking place a considerable distance away from the party wall.

Airborne dirt and dust is even more difficult than noise. When someone attacks a chimney stack without warning, causing massive falls of soot to emerge from next door's open fireplace, ruining their carpets (as happened to a well-known Lord Justice who forthwith appointed me to sort the matter out), it is pretty straightforward. However, general claims for 'extra cleaning' of carpets and curtains need much more careful scrutiny. It is not unreasonable to expect the adjoining owners to keep their windows shut when demolition, for example, is going on, even if the site is well damped down, but at the height of summer it is equally reasonable for those owners to want some air in their houses. In a recent job of mine, the developers installed air conditioning units next door to try to solve the problem – though for various reasons the adjoining owner still was not entirely happy.

It is both surveyors' jobs to strike the proper balance in all these matters, and to see that the adjoining owner is adequately recompensed for damage genuinely suffered. In my opinion, one should not stand too rigidly upon precise definition of the source of the problem when settling such claims, despite the strict legal constraints which I have set out above.

At the end of the whole job, when all the works affecting the party wall are complete, the schedule of condition should be checked to identify any damage which may have been caused by the works. *Prima facie*, any damage now seen which is not recorded in the schedule will be the responsibility of the building owner: it will be for him to prove that there is some other cause than his works. Occasionally there may be genuine doubt or disagreement over the cause of new damage, and again both surveyors must do their honest best correctly to ascertain the cause of the damage. If they cannot agree – and they should not automatically take the side of their appointing owner, but impartially seek the truth – they can call on the third surveyor to decide. I suppose that this, if not fees, is the most common cause of such referrals.

If the damage is found and agreed, the adjoining owner can choose under section 11 (8) whether to have it made good by the building owner or to take cash instead. Arguments over the cost of making good are quite common, and can be difficult to resolve, but all the remarks above about applying impartial expertise and judgement apply yet again.

Sometimes no one tells the building owner's surveyor that the party wall works are complete and, as I have said above, he may well not be in regular touch with the site. If he does not know, he cannot tell the adjoining owner's surveyor, who may be delaying his final site visit until he receives that information. It is a good idea for the building owner's surveyor to impress upon his side the need for him to be informed at the appropriate juncture. It is much more satisfactory for everyone if the party wall matters come to a definite conclusion rather than just peter out.

When security for expenses has been provided, that security must now be returned to the building owner. Any payments due to the adjoining owner having been made, the residue and all the interest earned belong to the original depositor. The security should not be regarded as the prime and proper source for the surveyors' fees or for payments under section 11 (8), unless the building owner either agrees or else fails to honour his obligations in another way.

The award should not now be discarded, since it may come in handy in the future, but it is not a deed, and is not binding for the future. An award deals strictly with the present circumstances, and is the expression of the views of the currently appointed surveyors. New surveyors, under new notices, may take different views with perfect propriety. In particular, however, the schedule of condition may be useful if claims of later appearing damage attribute the defects to the original works. On the whole, though, the award has done its work, and the surveyors may now retire from the scene to await their next party wall job – or get on with the ten others clamouring for their attention.

Definitions

Local Authority	The term 'Local Authority' is not defined in the Party Wall etc. Act, but will either be adopted from another Act or will be the subject of a one clause Amendment Act. In either case, it will be the authority exercising building control.
Owner	In effect, an owner is anyone with an interest greater than a yearly tenancy, including someone about to acquire such an interest, either as freeholder or leaseholder.
Party Structure/ Party Wall	A party structure includes a floor/ceiling separating flats from each other, maisonettes from shops, or offices from those below/above.

A wall is not party (either with or without the word 'fence' attached to it) just because the spread footings or other foundation projects across the boundary. Part of the wall itself must be astride the boundary, unless the second part, (b), of the definition comes into play.

A definition (b) makes it possible for a wall which is wholly on the land of, and wholly owned by, one owner to have party attributions, where another building encloses upon it. The legality of that enclosure is not addressed by the Act but to the extent – and to that extent only – that such a wall separates the buildings of two owners, it is party.

See *Figures 9, 10, 11 and 12.*

Surveyor Several attempts were made to define 'surveyor' in a non-exclusive way, but it was eventually decided, on the advice of the Department of the Environment (as it was), simply to ensure that an 'owner' could not nominate himself as his surveyor. It is almost impossible for an owner to be properly impartial in dealing with party wall matters, and the only person I can think of who could be so relied upon has always appointed someone else as my surveyor, when a notice was served or received.

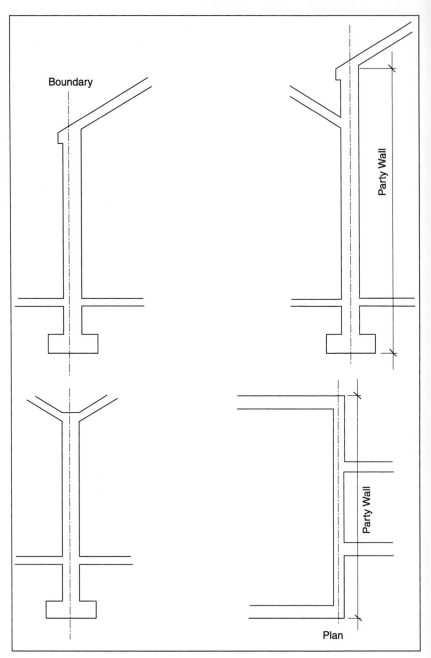

Figure 9: Party wall as defined in section 20(a)

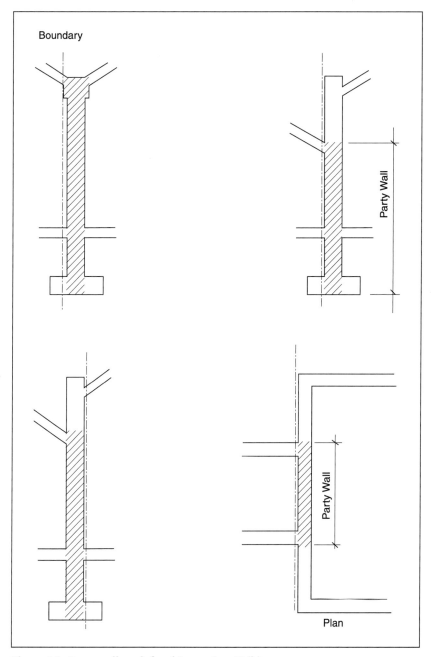

Figure 10: Party wall as defined in section 20(b)

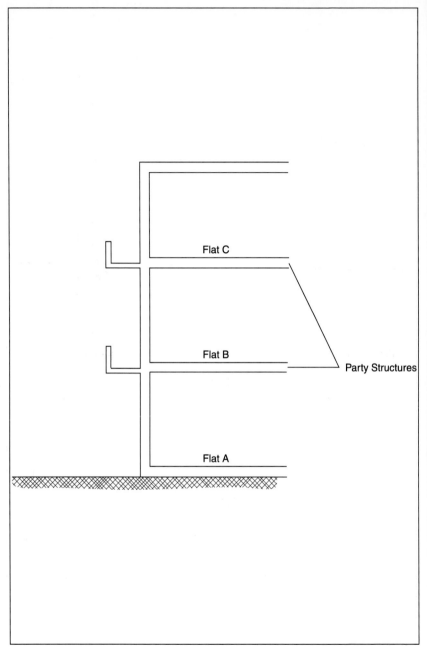

Figure 11: Party structure diagram section 20

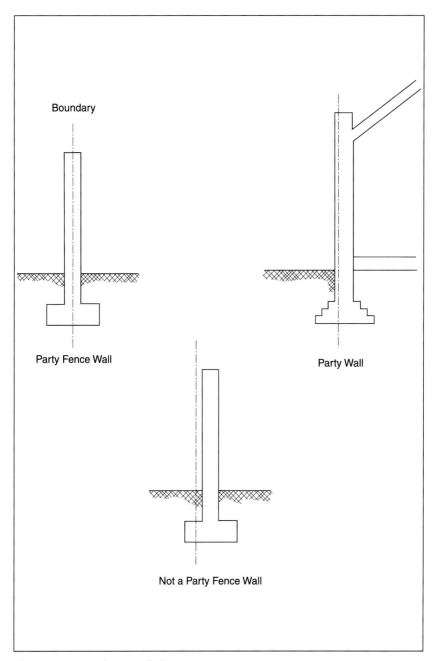

Figure 12: Party fence wall diagram section 20

Further reading and information

There are some essential books, and some useful books, which should be read in conjunction with this manual. In order of essentialness, they are:

The Pyramus and Thisbe Club (1996). *The Party Wall Act Explained: A Commentary on the Party Wall etc. Act (The Green Book)*.

This is published by The Pyramus and Thisbe Club and is a clause by clause commentary on the Act. It includes useful forms and precedents. It is written largely by those who drafted the Act.

Anstey, J. (1997). *An Introduction to the Party Wall etc. Act 1996*. Lark Publications.

This is published by Lark Productions in their 'Need To Know' series. It is another book commenting on the Act, but heavily slanted towards case law. As well as similar forms and precedents, it also includes summaries of about fifty leading cases.

Anstey, J. (1998). *Party Walls and What to do with Them*. RICS Books.

This is a narrative guide to the world of party walls, written in a light-hearted manner. It is now in its fifth edition, having been revised further even since the new Act came into being.

The Royal Institution of Chartered Surveyors (1996). *Party Wall Legislation and Procedure: A Guidance Note* (fourth edition). RICS Books.

The RICS guidance note on party walls has considerable input from The Pyramus and Thisbe Club, and is a very short introduction to the Act, with many forms and precedents.

Bickford-Smith, S. and Sydenham, C. (1997). *Party Walls: The New Law*. Jordan Publishing.

If you want a lawyer's approach to the Act, this is it. In my opinion it is not a good book for a party wall surveyor trying to follow the common-sense practices intended by the promoters of the Act, but if you are a lawyer seeking fine points on which to quibble, this is where to look.

Several other people have rushed into publication, but most of them have errors and very little to contribute. If you have all the books listed above, you should have all you need, while this manual alone plus *The Green Book* will equip you fairly well. *The Collected Papers of The Pyramus and Thisbe Club* are not essential reading, and some of them deal with subjects other than Party Walls, but they are very interesting in their relationship to the subject, and much of what is said about the London Building Acts (Amendment) Act 1939, is still true of the 1996 Act.

The Pyramus and Thisbe Club is the organization for party wall surveyors. It started as a small group of active surveyors in London, and grew steadily until the 1996 Act was passed, whereupon it expanded rapidly and sprouted several affiliated clubs in various parts of England and Wales. As I have mentioned, no particular qualification is demanded of members, only an enthusiasm for the subject and a willingness to share experiences with other members. Naturally, most of the members are surveyors (many of them chartered building surveyors), but architects, engineers and solicitors also belong.

Papers given at meetings are regularly published (and see *The Collected Papers* above) and an irregular newsletter 'Whispers Through Wall's Chink' also appears. By now you should have gathered that the Club is named after Shakespeare's famous lovers in *A Midsummer Night's Dream*, who conversed through a chink in the wall between their parents' properties. The motto of the Club is Bottom's comment to Duke Theseus, 'The wall is down that parted their fathers...'

A directory of members is available, organized by counties, so that Local Authorities, Citizens' Advice Bureaux and others, can find members in their respective areas. Prospective members can apply to The Pyramus and Thisbe Club, Administration Office, Florence House, 53 Acton Lane, London, NW10 8UX.

Index

Page numbers in *italics* refer to figures.

access/entry: rights 8, 38–9, 52
Access to Neighbouring Land Act 1992 8
acknowledgement of notices 27, 28
adjoining owners 9, 10, 12, 13–14
change 46, 48
    and expenses/damages 26, 61–2, 64
    and notice serving 17, 18, 21
        response to 25, 31, 34
agreed surveyors 31, 32–4, 35, 54
appeals 53, 54, 56–8
architect: and party wall duties 34
authority, surveyor's 10, *11*, 49–50, 63
awards 44, 47, 49, 50, 51–5
and fees 53, 56–7, 60

banks: and security expenses 29
building owner 9–10, 12, 32
    and award 51–2
    change 46–7, 48
    and notice serving 17–18, 34
    responsibilities/liability 12, 39, 44, 64

changes: of owner/plan 46–8
communications 21, 30–1, 43–5
condition, schedule of 38–42, 64
consent, obtaining/giving 25, *27*, 28, 30–1
Construction (Design and Management)
    regulations 10
counter-notices 26, *27, 28*
cracks, recording 41

damage: and compensation 64
defects, building: and expenses 61
dirt/dust 49, 63, 64
disputes 8, 17–18, 21, 30

engineers 15, 18, 43–4, 59
entry/access: rights 8, 38–9, 52
environmental health officers 52
excavation: under 1996 Act 15
expenses 61–2
    security for 26, 29, 65

fees 25, 53, 56–7, 59–60
forms: and notice serving 17, 21
foundations 47
and notices 18, *19–20, 24, 28*

Green Book 16, 72

hours of working, permitted 52

informality 21, 30–1, 44–5
instructions, taking 9–12

letter of authority 10, *11*
light, rights of 53
line of junction notice 17, *22*
local authority 52, 66
London Building Acts (Amendment) Act
    1939 8, 9, 30, 38

noise 49, 52, 63–4
notices
    checking: on receipt 25–9
    party structure 9, *23*
    serving 14, 16, 17–24, 32, 34
        and personal approach 21, 30–1
    three/six metre 18, *19–20, 24, 28*

owners 9, 12, 66–7 *see also* adjoining
    owners; building owner

party fence wall 17, 66, *71*
party structure 66, *70*
party structure notice 9, *23, 27*
party wall 17, 66, *68–9*
Party Wall etc. Act 1996 8, 9, 15, 33
    on appeals 57
    on costs/fees 31, 59, 61, 64, 65
    and disputes settlement 17–18, 21, 30
    on entry rights 38, 52
    on notices 16, 17–18, 21, 25–6
    on surveyors 10, 34, 36, 51
    specified sections:
    1   17–18, 61
    2   17, 18
    3   17, 18
    4   26
    6   17, 18, 25–6, 30, 63
    7   47
    8   38
    9   53
    10 10, 18, 36, 37, 57, 59
    11 26, 31, 61, 64, 65

specified sections (continued):
  12 26
  15 18, 21
  16 38, 52
plan, changes of 47, 48
progress: of works 63–5
Pyramus and Thisbe Club 36, 37, 73

risk: to adjoining owner 26, 31

schedule of condition 38–42, 64
security: for expenses 26, 29, 65
six metre notice 18, *20, 24, 28*

solicitors 25, 59
surveyors 10, 30–1, 32–5, 66–7
  adjoining owner's 25–6, 34–5, 52, 59–60
  agreed 31, 32–4, 35, 54
  building owner's 12, 41–2, 53, 60
    appointment 10, *11,* 32
    as party wall surveyor 10, 33–4, 49–50
    and works progress 63, 65
  third 26, 29, 53–4, 56–8, 60
    selection 36–7, 51

three metre notice 18, *19, 24, 28*